big NATE
THE CROWD GOES WILD!

More

big NATE

adventures from

LINCOLN PEIRCE

Novels:

Big Nate: In a Class by Himself
Big Nate Strikes Again
Big Nate On a Roll
Big Nate Goes for Broke
Big Nate Flips Out
Big Nate in the Zone

Activity Books:

Big Nate Boredom Buster
Big Nate Fun Blaster
Big Nate Doodlepalooza

Comic Compilations:

Big Nate From the Top
Big Nate Out Loud
Big Nate and Friends
Big Nate: What Could Possibly Go Wrong?
Big Nate: Here Goes Nothing
Big Nate Makes the Grade
Big Nate All Work and No Play
Big Nate Game On!
Big Nate: Genius Mode
Big Nate: I Can't Take It!
Big Nate: Great Minds Think Alike
Big Nate: Mr. Popularity

big NATE

THE CROWD GOES WILD!

by LINCOLN PEIRCE

SCHOLASTIC INC.

A FIFTY-DOLLAR REGISTRATION FEE JUST TO BE IN SOME CHEESY "BATTLE OF THE BANDS"? WHAT A **RIP-OFF!**

WELL, IT'S **THEIR** LOSS! THEY'LL MISS OUT ON OUR MUSIC!... OUR SHOWMANSHIP!... OUR LIGHT SHOW!

WAIT, WE HAVE A **LIGHT SHOW?**

CHAD WAS GOING TO STAND OFFSTAGE WITH A FLASHLIGHT.

SHOW US YOUR STROBE ACTION, DUDE.

KLIK
KLIK
KLIK
KLIK

SO NOW THAT WE'RE NOT DOING THE "BATTLE OF THE BANDS," WHAT'S OUR NEXT MOVE?

I'M NOT SURE.

BUT **SOME**HOW, **SOME** WAY, ENSLAVE THE MOLLUSK **WILL** BE **NOTICED!**

DUDE, WE'VE **ALREADY** BEEN NOTICED!

WE HAVE?

YEAH, REMEMBER THAT COP? AND THE WHOLE "DISTURBING THE PEACE" THING?

OHHHH YEAH!

ALL SET?

LET'S GO!

HANG ON, NATE! YOU FORGOT YOUR HELMET!

HELMET? DAD, IT'S ONLY **POND HOCKEY!**

THERE'S NO CHECKING, NO SLAP SHOTS...

THAT'S BESIDE THE POINT. ACCIDENTS CAN STILL HAPPEN.

YOU COULD SLIP AND FALL. YOU COULD COLLIDE WITH SOMEONE. YOU COULD TAKE A STICK IN THE TEETH.

THERE ARE A HUNDRED WAYS YOU COULD GET HURT PLAYING HOCKEY!

FLIP!

THONK!

A HUNDRED AND ONE.

TECHNICALLY, I DON'T THINK THIS COUNTS AS A HOCKEY INJURY.

THIS IS WHY I PREFER BASKETBALL.

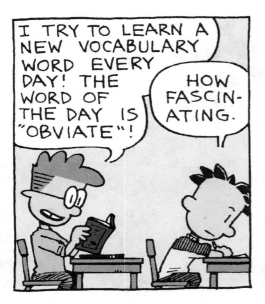

I HOPE MR. ROSA IS HAVING A BAD DAY TODAY!

WHAT? WHY?

BECAUSE IF HE'S HAVING A **GOOD** DAY, HE'LL BE ALL AMPED UP ABOUT SOME INCREDIBLY LAME PROJECT HE WANTS US TO DO!

...BUT IF HE'S HAVING A **BAD** DAY, HE'LL BE TOO STRESSED OUT TO DO ANY ACTUAL TEACHING! HE'LL LET US DO WHATEVER WE **WANT**!

HELLO, CLASS.

LOOKIN' GOOD!

Peirce

OH, GOODIE! IT'S ALMOST BOOK BUDDY TIME! THE BOOK BUDDIES ARE COMING!

I **LOVE** MY BOOK BUDDY! SHE SMELLS LIKE FLOWERS, AND SHE BRINGS ME PEPPERMINTS!

WHAT'S **YOUR** BOOK BUDDY LIKE?

I TRY NOT TO THINK ABOUT IT.

PETER, M'LAD!

PETER, YOU **RASCAL**! YOU NEVER TOLD ME YOU HAD A **GIRLFRIEND**!

SHE ISHN'T MY GIRL-FRIEND.

SHE'SH A **PESHT**, THAT'SH WHAT SHE ISH!

SHE **LIKES** YOU! WHAT'S SO BAD ABOUT **THAT**?

HI, PETER. I DON'T WANT YOU TO EAT LUNCH WITH AMANDA LIKE YOU DID YESTERDAY. I WANT YOU TO EAT LUNCH WITH **ME**!

EVERY DAY. FOREVER. UNTIL YOU **DIE**!

IT'SH NOT ALL IT'SH CRACKED UP TO BE.

I LOVE WALKING AROUND THE SCHOOL, GETTING TO KNOW THE STUDENTS!

IT'S SO MUCH FUN TO BE AROUND THEM, FEEDING OFF THEIR ENERGY AND ANSWERING THEIR QUESTIONS!

PRINCIPAL NICHOLS, HOW COME WE DON'T HAVE ANY HOT YOUNG SWEDISH STUDENT TEACHERS?

THEN AGAIN, THERE'S A LOT TO BE SAID FOR LOCKING MYSELF IN MY OFFICE WITH A JELLY DONUT.

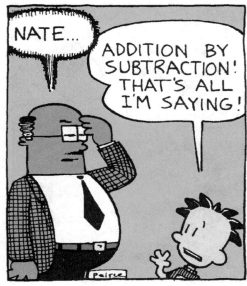

PRINCIPAL NICHOLS NEVER TAKES ANY OF MY SUGGESTIONS!

HOW ARE THINGS SUPPOSED TO GET ANY **BETTER** AROUND THIS STINKIN' DUMP IF NOTHING EVER **CHANGES?**

WELL, PERHAPS AN ATTITUDE ADJUSTMENT ON THE PART OF **SOME** PEOPLE WOULD BE HELPFUL.

GOOD POINT. HE'S SO **NEGA-TIVE.**

Peirce

... SO IF WE WIN TOMORROW, WE'RE IN THE PLAYOFFS?

RIGHT!

BUT WHAT IF COOLIDGE WINS **THEIR** GAME?

IT DOESN'T MATTER WHAT OTHER TEAMS DO! WE CONTROL OUR OWN DESTINY!

ARRGH!

WHAT?

THAT EXPRESSION! "WE CONTROL OUR OWN DESTINY"!

WHAT ABOUT IT?

IT MAKES **NO SENSE!** YOU CAN'T **CONTROL** DESTINY!

IF SOMETHING IS **DESTINED**, IT'S **PRE-DETERMINED!** IT'S A **CERTAINTY!**

TO TALK ABOUT CONTROLLING DESTINY IS JUST **STUPID!**

SO... DESTINY IS WHEN SOMETHING **MUST** HAPPEN?

RIGHT.

FIVE SECONDS LATER...

I HAD TO DO IT.

NO DOUBT.

34

DAD, THIS IS RYAN. HE JUST MOVED HERE!

HI, RYAN!

YOU BOYS LOOK HUNGRY! CAN I GET YOU A SNACK?

SURE! THANK YOU VERY MUCH!

OKAY, LET'S SEE HERE. WE'VE GOT SOME PRUNES... A FEW PACKAGES OF INSTANT OATMEAL... SOME CHOPPED WALNUTS...

DO YOU LIKE DILL PICKLES? OH, AND WE HAVE CARROTS AND CELERY. YOU CAN DIP THEM IN SOY SAUCE.

HOW ABOUT SOME ZESTY RANCH CROUTONS? AND HERE'S AN OLIVE LOAF THAT'S STILL FRESH!

THAT'S A LOT OF CHOICES, GUYS! JUST TELL ME WHAT YOU...

? ?

WHERE'D HE GO?

YOU'RE COSTING ME FRIENDS.

Peirce

SO WHAT BRINGS YOU TO TOWN, UNCLE TED?

JUST FULFILLING MY FAMILIAL DUTIES, NATE.

YOU AND YOUR SISTER ARE GROWING UP FAST, AND AS YOUR UNCLE, I WANT TO SHARE IN THE JOYS OF YOUR CHILDHOOD!

OH.

WHAT JOYS ARE WE TALKING ABOUT?

QUIET, LAD. I'M WATCHING "WHEEL."

Peirce

HELLO? HEY, FRANCIS.

NO, I CAN'T. MY UNCLE'S HERE.

HM?... YEAH, YOU MET HIM LAST YEAR ON NEW YEAR'S EVE, REMEMBER?

HA HA HA HA HA HA HA HA

YUP! THAT'S HIM!

YEAH, HE'S STILL GOT THE UNICORN HAIRCUT!

I MAY MOVE INTO A MOTEL.

HA HA HA HA HA HA HA

Peirce

I'M GOING TO THROW SOME SUPPER TOGETHER, TED. FEEL LIKE PEELING A FEW POTATOES?

AH. SADLY, NO.

I'M AFRAID MY BADLY INJURED RIGHT WRIST **PROHIBITS** ME FROM PERFORMING SUCH TASKS!

BUT YOU JUST SPENT ALL AFTERNOON PLAYING **HALO!**

EXACTLY. HOW DO YOU THINK I HURT MY WRIST?

THE BOY'S NOT VERY BRIGHT, IS HE?

HOW ABOUT YOU PEEL LEFTY?

ARE YOU ENJOYING UNCLE TED'S VISIT, NATE?

HM? OH. YEAH, SURE.

I WANT TO MAKE SURE YOU UNDERSTAND, THOUGH, THAT TED ISN'T... UH... HE'S NOT... I MEAN, YOU SHOULDN'T.... UMM...

SON, UNCLE TED ISN'T A GOOD ROLE MODEL.

I FIGURED THAT OUT ALREADY, DAD.

WHAT'S YOUR COMPUTER PASSWORD?

MUNCH MUNCH MUNCH

CRISPY CHUNK

peirce

HEY, **WRIGHT!** I **CHALLENGE** YOU!

HM?

YOU'RE MISTER **TRASH TALK,** AREN'T YOU? LET'S **GO!**

FINE. GO AHEAD.

OKAY! ✷AHEM!✷... YOU'RE SO DUMB, YOU CAN'T EVEN READ AN **AUDIO** BOOK!

HEH HEH HA HA HA HA HEH HA

YOU'RE SO UGLY, YOUR FACE MAKES **ONIONS** CRY!

HA HA HEH HA

YOU'RE SO SHORT, WHEN IT RAINS YOU'RE ALWAYS THE LAST TO KNOW!

HA HA HEH GOOD ONE, RANDY!

WHAT DO YOU SAY TO **THAT?**

YOU'RE SO PATHETIC, YOU RECYCLE LAME INSULTS FROM THE INTERNET AND PRETEND YOU WERE BRIGHT ENOUGH TO THINK THEM UP YOURSELF.

WA HA HA HA HA HA HA HA HA HA HA HA

I THOUGHT YOU WERE GOING TO **CHALLENGE** ME!

PRINCIPAL NICHOLS! CAN I TALK TO YOU ABOUT SOMETHING?

IF YOU CAN BE BRIEF, NATE. I HAVE A MEETING.

YEAH, OKAY.

IT'S ABOUT MY LEGACY AS CLASS PRESIDENT. WHEN PEOPLE ANALYZE MY ADMINISTRATION IN FUTURE YEARS...

THE SECRET IS TO NEVER STOP WALKING.

...SEEMS REASONABLE TO ME THAT SOME SORT OF COMMEMORATIVE PLAQUE IS IN ORDER.

Peirce

IF YOU'RE WONDERING ABOUT YOUR LEGACY, WHY NOT JUST **ASK** PEOPLE?

YEAH, TAKE A SURVEY!

HMM!

GREETINGS, CITIZENS! WHAT DO YOU THINK MY LEGACY AS CLASS PRESIDENT WILL BE?

SLAM!

THE PEOPLE HAVE SPOKEN!

ACTUALLY, THEY DIDN'T SAY ALL THAT MUCH.

KEEP OUR SCHOOL CLEAN

MRS. SHIPULSKI, DO YOU THINK I'VE BEEN A GOOD CLASS PRESIDENT?

CHILD, YOU'RE THE BEST PRESIDENT THIS SCHOOL'S EVER HAD!

I AM?

ABSOLUTELY! LAST WEDNESDAY **CONFIRMED** IT!

HE GAVE ME A BOX OF "SNO-CAPS" FOR SECRETARY'S DAY.

I MADE A LIST OF ALL MY ACCOMPLISHMENTS AS CLASS PRESIDENT!

I DON'T MEAN TO BRAG, BUT IT'S PRETTY IMPRESSIVE!

LEMME SEE.

"SCHOOL PERFORMED BETTER IN STANDARDIZED TESTING THIS YEAR"? HOW IS THAT **YOUR** ACCOMPLISHMENT?

I INSPIRE PEOPLE, FRANCIS.

WEREN'T YOU ABSENT ON STANDARDIZED-TESTING DAY?

LET'S GO TEDDY COME ON BABY PITCH IT RIGHT IN THERE IN THERE RIGHT DOWN THE PIKE KID RIGHT DOWN BROADWAY **SWING** BATTER!

ATTA BOY ATTA BABY I'VE SEEN BETTER LOOKING SWINGS IN MY BACKYARD HE CAN'T HE CAN'T HE CAN'T HIT HE'S WAY BEHIND YOU KID C'MON NOW TEDDY PUT IT RIGHT PAST HIM HE'S NO BATTER NO BATTER **SWING** BATTER!

THAT'S ALL RIGHT TEDDY THAT'S ALL RIGHT KID YOU GOT THIS GUY JUST THROW STRIKES BABY JUST ROCK AND FIRE KID ROCK AND FIRE HE'S LOOKIN FOR A WALK HE CAN'T HIT HE'S NO BATTER NO BATTER NO BATTER C'MON BABY HIT THE MITT JUST HIT THE MITT FOCUS ON THE MITT KID ATTA BOY LET'S GET THIS KID NOW LET'S PUT HIM IN THE BOOKS SIT HIM DOWN TEDDY SIT HIM DOWN HE'S AFRAID OF YOU TEDDY HE CAN'T HIT HE'S NO BATTER NO BATTER NO BATTER NO BATTER **SWING** BATTER!

FEEL THE BREEZE FEEL THE BREEZE HE'S BEHIND YOU TEDDY HE'S WAY BEHIND YOU JUST ONE MORE BABY JUST ONE MORE PUT IT RIGHT PAST HIM TEDDY PUT IT RIGHT PAST HIM YOU AND THE GLOVE KID JUST YOU AND THE GLOVE HE'S NO BATTER NO BATTER NO BATTER HE CAN'T HIT

WILL YOU **SHUT UP!**

JUST FOR THIS BATTER, OR FOR THE WHOLE INNING?

FOREVER!

HE'S HAVING A ROUGH DAY.

Peirce

HOLD IT, FRANCIS! COOL YOUR JETS!

WHAT?

EVERY TIME YOU GET A NEW COPY OF THE "BOOK OF FACTS," YOU SPEND **DAYS** READING US ALL SORTS OF USELESS TRIVIA!

OKAY, OKAY, I WON'T DO THAT.

I'LL ONLY READ YOU THE **GOOD** STUFF!

KILL ME NOW.

DID YOU KNOW THAT THE PRO PULATION OF HE UNITED S N THE YEAR S 420 MILLIO AN INCREASE ALMOST 70 M

Peirce

DO YOU KNOW WHEN THE NEXT TOTAL SOLAR ECLIPSE IN THE U.S. WILL OCCUR?

AUGUST 21ST, 2017! DO YOU KNOW WHO WON THE NOBEL PRIZE FOR PHYSICS IN 1949?

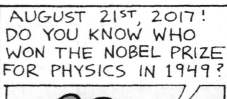

HIDEKI YUKAWA! DO YOU KNOW WHAT COUNTRY RANKS FIFTH IN RENEWABLE WATER RESOURCES PER CAPITA?

PAPUA NE_
AND DO
WHICH
COMPL
PATIEN
VISITIN
EMERG
ROOMS

THE "JUST IGNORE HIM" STRATEGY ISN'T WORKING.

LET'S EXPLORE THE WEDGIE OPTION.

DID YOU KNOW THAT THE SUN CONTAINS 99.86 PERCENT OF THE TOTAL MASS OF OUR ENTIRE SOLAR SYSTEM?

NO, I DIDN'T KNOW THAT. BUT YOU JUST TOLD ME. SO NOW I KNOW.

OOP. I JUST FORGOT IT. WHAT A SHAME.

WANT ME TO READ IT AGAI—

NO!

DID YOU KNOW THAT THE STATE MOTTO OF NEW MEXICO IS...

YES, FRANCIS! YOU TOLD US YESTERDAY! "CRESCIT EUNDO"!

OH NO!

YOU AND YOUR STUPID BOOK OF FACTS! I'M ACTUALLY STARTING TO REMEMBER THIS STUFF!

YOU'RE INFECTING ME!

TROUBLE. TROUBLE. TROUBLE. TROUBLE.

Peirce

THIS SOCIAL STUDIES TEST IS GONNA BE **BRUTAL!**

I KNOW.

HEY, LET'S ALL STUDY TOGETHER!

COME ON OVER TO MY HOUSE AFTER SUPPER, AND WE'LL HAVE A "CRAM SESSION"!

BRING YOUR CLASS NOTES! IT'LL BE A **BLAST!**

FUN GUY.

IF I **HAD** CLASS NOTES, I WOULDN'T **NEED** TO STUDY WITH FRANCIS.

OKAY, GUYS, WE'VE GOT A LOT TO COVER HERE, SO LET'S GET STARTED.

I'VE CREATED A TIMELINE DETAILING ALL THE EVENTS THAT ARE GOING TO BE COVERED ON THE TEST! HERE ARE YOUR COPIES!

LOOK AT THEM CAREFULLY AND TELL ME IF YOU HAVE ANY QUESTIONS.

YES?

WHEN YOU SAID WE WERE GOING TO STUDY IN THE KITCHEN, I ASSUMED THERE'D BE SNACKS.

TO HELP MYSELF REMEMBER STUFF, SOMETIMES I MAKE UP LITTLE RHYMES!

THOMAS PAINE SAID: "I'M NOT DENSE! I'LL WRITE A BOOK CALLED COMMON SENSE!"

TRY IT!

OKAY. UMMM...

FORT TICONDEROGA WAS IN NEW YORK...

...AND FRANCIS IS A TOTAL DORK!

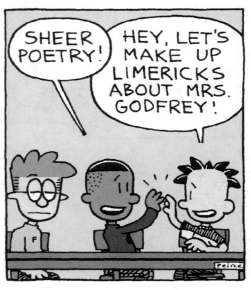

SHEER POETRY!

HEY, LET'S MAKE UP LIMERICKS ABOUT MRS. GODFREY!

1765 - Stamp Act
1773 - Boston Tea Party
1775 - Paul Revere's Ride
1776 - Declaration of
        Independence
1777 - Ticonderoga
        edict Arnold
        Yo   wn
        ris   te Treaty

YOU'RE UP THIRD THIS INNING, NATE.

TIME TO BREAK OUT OF THIS STUPID SLUMP.

I HAVEN'T HAD A HIT IN **FOUR GAMES**!

FIVE, ACTUALLY...

...DURING WHICH TIME YOUR AVERAGE HAS PLUMMETED FROM AN ACCEPTABLE .290 TO AN ANEMIC .225.

BUT GOOD LUCK ANYWAY!

I COULD DO WITHOUT THE ADJECTIVES, STAT BOY.

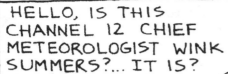

HELLO, IS THIS CHANNEL 12 CHIEF METEOROLOGIST WINK SUMMERS?... IT IS?

WINK, WHAT'S UP WITH THIS **RAIN**? YOU DIDN'T SAY IT WAS GOING TO **RAIN** IN YOUR FORECAST!

THIS STUPID RAIN WASHED OUT MY BALLGAME AND COST ME A **HOME RUN!**

HELLO?

I DON'T THINK CELL PHONES ARE SUPPOSED TO GET WET.

Peirce

NATE "SCOOP" WRIGHT HERE, MR. GALVIN! CAN I INTERVIEW YOU FOR THE SCHOOL PAPER?

I SUPPOSE.

HAVE YOU MET THE SUBSTITUTE FRENCH TEACHER? MADAME BENOIT?

NO, I HAVEN'T.

I HEAR SHE RUNS MARATHONS!

THAT'S VERY ADMIRABLE.

YOU NEED STRONG LEGS FOR THAT!

INDEED.

DON'T THEY CALL FRENCH A ROMANCE LANGUAGE?

THAT'S RIGHT.

DO **YOU** SPEAK FRENCH?

NO. I'VE ALWAYS WANTED TO LEARN.

OKAY! THANKS!

GALVIN ADMIRES BENOIT'S LEGS, CRAVES ROMANCE

TIK TIK TIK

HAVE YOU NOTICED HOW THIS AWESOME WEATHER IS PUTTING EVERYONE IN A GREAT MOOD?

LIKE **JENNY**, FOR EXAMPLE! SHE LOOKS LIKE... LIKE...

...LIKE SHE KNOWS ARTUR'S GETTING BACK FROM TURKEY NEXT WEEK?

Peirce

JENNY, M'LADY!

I'M NOT YOUR LADY.

RELAX, JENNY, IT'S JUST AN EXPRESSION! SAYING "M'LADY" IS A FORM OF **RESPECT!** IT'S **CHIVALRY!**

RIGHT. SO YOU'RE CHIVALROUS.

NOPE. I'M CHIVALICIOUS.

EW.

EWW.

EW.

ex**CUSE** ME, WHO **ASKED** YOU?

SO! JENNY! I HEAR ARTUR'S GETTING BACK FROM TURKEY SOON!

YUP.

CAN I ASK YOU SOMETHING AS A FRIEND? WHAT IF, HYPOTHETICALLY, ARTUR DECIDED TO... AND I'M ONLY ASKING THIS AS A FRIEND...

WHAT IF ARTUR ENDED UP... AND I'M JUST SAYING THIS AS A FRIEND... WHAT IF HE ENDED UP FINDING A NEW GIRLFRIEND OVER THERE?

REMEMBER, THIS IS TOTALLY HYPOTHETICAL.

LIKE OUR FRIENDSHIP.

LOOK, JENNY, ALL I'M SAYING IS, IT'S NOT LIKE YOU AND ARTUR ARE GONNA GO OUT **FOREVER!**

MAYBE WE **WILL!**

...OR MAYBE WE **WON'T!** HOW SHOULD **I** KNOW? WHY **WORRY** ABOUT IT?

I JUST TRY TO ENJOY TODAY. TOMORROW, **ANY**THING CAN HAPPEN!

ANY-THING?

EXCEPT THAT.

NUTS.

Peirce

ARTUR'S GETTING BACK TOMORROW!

YES, AND WHAT'S THE BIG DEAL?

ALL HE DID WAS GO TO TURKEY FOR SIX MONTHS! EVERYBODY'S ACTING LIKE HE'S A **HERO** OR SOMETHING!

MAYBE **I'LL** GO TO TURKEY! THEN EVERYBODY WILL THROW A PARADE FOR **ME!**

EXCEPT IN **YOUR** CASE, WE'LL HAVE THE PARADE WHEN YOU **LEAVE!**

RIMSHOT!

DANG IT!

TIK!

MULLIGAN.

HOLD IT, DAD.

YOU TOLD ME NOT TO LET YOU TAKE ANY MULLIGANS.

I DID?

YOU SAID YOU WANTED TO PLAY A 100% LEGITIMATE ROUND OF GOLF.

HOL PAR

AND YOU MADE ME PROMISE TO SAY SOMETHING IF I SAW YOU BREAKING ANY RULES.

WELL, I SHOULDN'T HAVE DONE THAT, NATE! THAT WASN'T FAIR TO YOU!

I CAN'T ASK **YOU** TO BE RESPONSIBLE FOR WHAT **I** DO!

SON, I WANT YOU TO **FORGET** THAT SELFISH REQUEST I MADE OF YOU!

OOP!

PRACTICE SWING!

WHIFF

✳SIGH..✳

Peirce

SO HOW WAS TURKEY, ARTUR?

VERY NICE. VERY BEAUTIFUL COUNTRY.

OF COURSE, BECAUSE I AM NOT **KNOW** ANYBODY THERE, I WAS FEELING MANY TIMES LONELY.

BUT ALWAYS I AM TO KNOW: AT LEAST I HAVE WONDERFUL **GIRLFRIEND** BACK IN USA!

THAT MUST BE A NICE FEELING TO HAVE.

HA! AND ALSO WHILE I WAS IN TURKEY, I AM MISSING NATE'S FUNNY **FACIAL EXPRESSINGS!**

Peirce

IT'S GOOD TO HAVE ARTUR BACK!

YUP!

UH-HUH.

AND... UH... LOOKS LIKE HE AND JENNY ARE STILL CRAZY ABOUT EACH OTHER.

YEAH. SO?

YOU GUYS THINK I STILL LIKE JENNY, BUT THAT SHIP HAS **SAILED!** THAT CRUSH IS **OVER!** I ONLY LIKE HER AS A **FRIEND** NOW!

FIVE... FOUR... THREE... TWO...

OF COURSE, I RESERVE THE RIGHT TO CHANGE MY MIND!

ARRGH! THE SOCIAL STUDIES FINAL IS GONNA **KILL** ME! I JUST CAN'T REMEMBER ALL THE NAMES AND DATES!

WANT ME TO QUIZ YOU?

DO WHATEVER YOU WANT. IT'S NOT GOING TO HELP.

WHEN WAS THE BATTLE OF VICKSBURG?

UHHHH... I DUNNO.

WHO WAS JOHN BROWN?

WHAT WAS THE HOMESTEAD ACT?

NO IDEA.

IT...UMM... I'M NOT SURE.

WHERE DID THE DRAFT RIOTS OF 1863...

I DON'T **KNOW**, FRANCIS! I'M TELLING YOU, MY BRAIN'S NOT **WIRED** THAT WAY!

WHO WORE NUMBER 39 FOR THE 1964 BOSTON RED SOX?

DALTON JONES!

YOU WERE SAYING?

OKAY, SO MAYBE THE WIRING'S OKAY, BUT THE CONTENT FILTER IS ALL SCREWED UP.

WHAT'S UP, DAD?

✵GRUNT!✵ I'M JUST TRYING TO GET IN SHAPE.

I WANT TO FEEL HEALTHIER! I WANT TO **LOOK** HEALTHIER!

WELL, THEN, MAYBE YOU SHOULD CHANGE INTO A DIFFERENT SHIRT.

HM? WHY?

JUST TRUST ME ON THIS ONE.

BUT AREN'T STRIPES SUPPOSED TO BE SLIMMING?

DAD, IF YOU WANT TO GET IN SHAPE, YOU NEED A PERSONAL TRAINER!

THAT'S TOO EXPENSIVE.

NO, IT ISN'T! I'LL DO IT! I'LL TRAIN YOU!

YOU?

SURE! I'LL DRAW UP AN EXERCISE PLAN! I'LL KEEP YOU FOCUSED! I'LL BRING DISCIPLINE TO YOUR LIFE!

...SAID THE C-PLUS STUDENT WHO CAN'T FIND THE CLOTHES HAMPER.

...AND I'LL DO IT FOR ONLY TEN BUCKS AN HOUR!

HERE'S WHY I'M THE IDEAL PERSONAL TRAINER FOR YOU, DAD: I **KNOW** YOU!

I KNOW YOU PUT FOUR SUGARS IN YOUR MORNING COFFEE... I KNOW YOU BUY POP-TARTS FROM THE VENDING MACHINE AT WORK...

I KNOW YOU MAKE YOURSELF A ROOT BEER FLOAT EVERY NIGHT AFTER I GO TO BED...

I THINK I'D RATHER HAVE A PERSONAL TRAINER WHO'S A BIT LESS PERSONAL.

...SURPRISING WHEN I FOUND YOUR SECRET STASH OF GUMMI WORMS!

OKAY, DAD, THAT'S ENOUGH STRETCHING. TIME FOR SOME REAL EXERCISE.

BUT I'M STILL GETTING LOOSE!

YOU'RE STALLING, DAD. LET'S GO. CHOP CHOP.

I'M NOT **STALLING**, I'M WARMING UP!

HONK

I'M WARM.

WE PERSONAL TRAINERS LIKE TO ROCK THE AIR HORN.

END-OF-THE-YEAR RE-CAP!

with your hosts:

BIFF BIFFWELL! & CHIP CHIPSON!

Well, Chip, the school year is almost over at P.S. 38!

Right, Biff! So let's take a look back at some of the exciting **HIGHLIGHTS!**

Uh... Walt? Where's the video? Can we see some highlights?

Sorry, Biff, there **ARE** no highlights. That's how boring this place is.

Good point.

What about **CURRENT** stuff? Is there anything happening right NOW? **ANY**thing?

Um... well, Mrs. Godfrey just finished grading the social studies exams and she's handing them back.

GREAT! Let's go there... **LIVE!**

THIS IS A NEW LOW.

I'M DEAD.

NATE, I'D LIKE TO TALK TO YOU. PRANK DAY IS TOMORROW, AND...

"PRANK DAY"?

I DON'T THINK I'M FAMILIAR WITH IT. "PRANK DAY," YOU SAY? HMMMM...

OH! YOU MEAN WHEN KIDS PLAY HARMLESS TRICKS, LIKE PUTTING FOOD COLORING IN THE WATER FOUNTAINS, OR DEFLATING THE BASKET-BALLS, OR...

...OR RELEASING A PACK OF RACCOONS IN THE FACULTY LOUNGE?

I KNOW NOTHING.

NICE TIMING, ARTUR! YOU GOT BACK FROM TURKEY JUST IN TIME FOR **PRANK DAY**!

PRANK DAY?

BUT... I AM NOT SO GOODS AT THINKING OF PRANKS.

I CAN HELP YOU THERE, ARTUR.

SEE THAT DOOR? THAT'S THE FACULTY BATHROOM.

AND SEE THIS? THIS IS A GIANT TUB OF MARSHMALLOW FLUFF.

LISTEN AND LEARN, ARTUR.

RRRIINNGG!

OKAY, PRANK DAY'S STARTED! WHAT'S YOUR FIRST TRICK?

JUST WAIT...

ATTENTION, PLEASE, THIS IS PRINCIPAL NICHOLS WITH A FEW WORDS OF WARNING ABOUT PRANK DAY.

THERE WILL BE SERIOUS CONSEQUENCES FOR ANY STUDENT WHO DE...

GAAH!

OH, THAT IS DIS**GUST**ING!

GAME ON!

PRANK DAY IS **AWESOME**!

✲CHUCKLE!✲ I JUST THREW A WATER BALLOON INTO THE GIRLS' LOCKER ROOM!

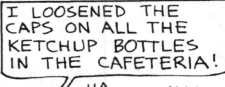

I LOOSENED THE CAPS ON ALL THE KETCHUP BOTTLES IN THE CAFETERIA!

HA HA!

YAWNN...

I SET UP AN INTERNET DATING ACCOUNT FOR MRS. GODFREY AND ARRANGED A MEETING FOR HER WITH A LOVESICK RODEO CLOWN.

HI, KIDS, WHICH WAY TO ROOM 213?

KEEP TRYING, BOYS.

peirce

MR. GALVIN, WILL YOU SIGN MY YEARBOOK?

MM-HM.

SIGN IT: "TO NATE, MY MOST GIFTED STUDENT"!

NO, WAIT! SIGN IT: "TO NATE, THE MOST BRILLIANT STUDENT I'VE EVER HAD"!

OR HOW ABOUT: "TO NATE, A GENIUS REMINISCENT OF A YOUNG EINSTEIN!"

"TO NATE, A STUPENDOUS..."

HERE.

WHAT'S THIS?

YOUR FINAL EXAM.

YOU CAN JUST WRITE "HAVE A GOOD SUMMER."

I'LL DO THAT.

Peirce

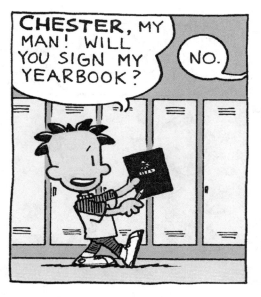

CHESTER, MY MAN! WILL YOU SIGN MY YEARBOOK?

NO.

I HATE SIGNING YEARBOOKS, AND I HATE YOU. SO HERE'S WHAT I'LL DO INSTEAD:

I'LL WRITE MY NAME ON YOUR FACE WITH A "SHARPIE." AND IF YOU HOLD STILL WHILE I'M DOING IT, I WON'T PUNCH YOU.

UNDER THE CIRCUMSTANCES, I FEEL LUCKY HE DIDN'T WRITE IT USING MY OWN BLOOD.

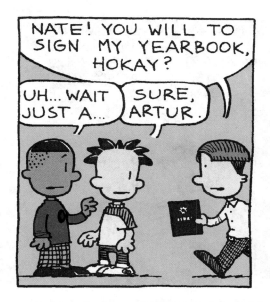

NATE! YOU WILL TO SIGN MY YEARBOOK, HOKAY?

UH... WAIT JUST A...

SURE, ARTUR.

Artur,
   You're a good kid. Have a great summer. I'm sure you've already got a lot of plans to hang out with Jenny, assuming you guys don't break up over the summer. Ha Ha, just kidding.

All I'm saying is, you never know what can happen. You could be an awesome couple one day, and the next day it's Dump City. Don't be surprised if Jenny decides to move i̶n̶ a different directi̶o̶ ember, A I've k̶ ̶onger an you h̶ and s̶ knows̶ ecause th you ne̶ ll. That' l I'm tr̶y to say, if

I TRIED TO WARN YOU, ARTUR.

I'M GOING TO NEED SOME MORE PAPER.

YOU'VE CERTAINLY GOT A LOT OF SIGNATURES IN YOUR YEARBOOK!

MM-HM.

"NATE: YOU ARE JUST LIKE MY OWN SON." **WOW**! WHO WROTE **THAT**?

MRS. CZERWICKI.

WHAT A NICE THING FOR HER TO SAY!

NOT REALLY. HER SON'S IN PRISON.

AH.

DETENTION MONITORS ARE SUCH A RIOT.

Peirce

HELLO?... OH, HEY DAD... YUP, WE ARRIVED SAFELY.

HM?... I WAS **GOING** TO CALL YOU! WE JUST **GOT** HERE!

OKAY... BYE.

BRRINNG!

HELLO? YUP, I WAS JUST ABOUT TO PUT ON SUNSCREEN.

YES, I'LL RE-APPLY AFTER I GO IN THE WATER!

BYE.

BRRINNG!

HELLO?...

I **KNOW**, I KNOW! I WON'T SWIM RIGHT AFTER I EAT!... HUH?... OF **COURSE** THERE'S A LIFEGUARD ON DUTY!

BYE!

BRRINNG!

YES, I'LL CALL YOU WHEN WE'RE ABOUT TO LEAVE!

I DON'T **KNOW** WHAT TIME!... **LATER!**

BOOP!

BRRINNG!

EVER SINCE I GOT A CELL PHONE, A DAY AT THE BEACH IS NO DAY AT THE BEACH.

HI, MOM.

AM I WEARING **WHAT**? CLEAN **UNDER-WEAR?**

GREAT.

OF COURSE ON THE DAY I FORGET MY CAP, IT **RAINS**.

BUT WILL THEY CALL OFF THE GAME? NO!

WHY **SHOULD** THEY? THEY'VE ALL GOT RAIN-COATS AND UMBRELLAS!

SO WHILE **THEY'RE** SITTING IN THE BLEACHERS ALL NICE AND DRY, **WE** STAND HERE GET-TING...

SMAK!

DAD! DID YOU SEE THAT?!

YOUR KID'S SAYING SOMETHING.

HM?

I KNOCKED 'EM ALL DOWN! I **WIN**!

NICE JOB, KID. PICK A PRIZE.

I'LL TAKE THAT RADIO!

THE RADIO'S A LEVEL **Q** PRIZE, DUDE. YOU NEED TO WIN A FEW MORE TIMES TO PICK **THAT**.

HOW MANY MORE?

FUN! FUN!

MAYBE IN CARNY SPEAK, EIGHT HUNDRED **IS** A FEW!

CONGRATS ON YOUR LEVEL A PLASTIC CHANGE PURSE!

A **HUNDRED BUCKS** IF YOU CAN REACH THE TOP OF THE CLIMBING WALL, KID!

WOW!

DON'T DO IT.

I JUST TOOK PICTURES OF THE WALL AND PLOTTED THEM AGAINST A DIMENSIONAL GRID ON MY PHONE.

IT'S ONLY POSSIBLE TO REACH THE TOP IF YOU HAVE A WING-SPAN IN EXCESS OF NINETY-TWO INCHES.

CRIPES.

EVERY SO OFTEN, FRANCIS, I'M GLAD YOU'RE A MATH GEEK!

HEY, I REMEMBER YOU! YOU USED TO RUN ONE OF THE **KIDDIE** RIDES!

YUP.

NOW YOU'RE ON THE "**WICKED TWISTED**"! THEY GAVE YOU A **PROMOTION**!

NOT REALLY.

WHATTA YA MEAN? THIS RIDE IS SO MUCH **BETTER**!

NOBODY EVER GOT SICK ON THE "BUMPITY BUNNY," KID.

WE NEED THE HOSE, DWAYNE.

PETER, I'M GOING TO WORK.

VERY WELL, MOTHER. THE LOVELY ALLISHON AND I WILL KEEP OURSHELVESH AMUSHED.

HONEY, ALLISON'S AWAY THIS WEEK. I GOT YOU A DIFFERENT SITTER.

WHICH ONE?

PETER, M'LAD!

SHOMEDAY I'M GOING TO REPORT THAT WOMAN TO SHOCIAL SHERVICESH.

WELL, ENOUGH SMALL TALK! GOT ANY SNACKS?

COME ON, PETER! LET'S GO OUTSIDE AND PLAY CATCH!

I'M READING.

BUT I PROMISED YOUR MOTHER YOU'D GET SOME EXERCISE!

I **AM** EXERCISHING! I'M EXERCISHING MY **BRAIN!**

I'M TALKING ABOUT **REAL** EXERCISE! STUFF THAT MAKES YOU **SWEAT!**

ANYTHING THAT INVOLVESH THROWING A BALL MAKESH MY PALMSH MOISHT.

THAT'S THE SPIRIT! I'LL MEET YOU OUT THERE!

Peirce

LET'S **GO**, PETER! BASEBALL TIME!

WAIT, WHY ARE YOU WEARING A **BIKE HELMET**?

SHIMPLY A PRECAUTION.

THE **LASHT** TIME A BABYSITTER MADE ME **EXERCISHE**, SHE REPEATEDLY THREW A **PLASHTIC DISHK** AT MY HEAD!

THAT WAS A FRISBEE, PETER.

NEEDLESSH TO SHAY, I HAD MOTHER FIRE HER IMMEDI- ATELY.

HOLD IT, HOLD IT. WHERE'S YOUR GLOVE?

WHY WOULD I HAVE A GLOVE? I **LOATHE** SHPORTSH!

OKAY, THEN, HERE! YOU CAN USE **MY** GLOVE!

IF I MUSHT, I MUSHT.

JUSHT A MINUTE! THISH ISHN'T **YOUR** GLOVE! THISH APPARENTLY BELONGSH TO SHOMEONE NAMED **DUSHTIN PEDROIA**!

PETER, WE NEED TO HAVE A LITTLE TALK.

FINE. TALKING ISH PREFERABLE TO THISH **BASHEBALL** NONSHENSHE!

Peirce

138

boop beep
beep boop
boop
beep

HI, IS THIS ACTION NEWS CHIEF METEOROLOGIST WINK SUMMERS?

WINK! NATE WRIGHT HERE!

LISTEN, WINK, WHAT WAS GOING ON DURING LAST NIGHT'S FORECAST? IT WAS LIKE YOU WERE IN A **COMA!**

AND IT WASN'T JUST **LAST** NIGHT! YOU JUST DON'T SEEM THAT **INTO** IT LATELY!

YOU USED TO BE **EXCITED** ABOUT THE WEATHER, WINK! YOUR FORECASTS WERE "MUST SEE" VIEWING!

BUT NOW YOU'RE ALL "HO HUM, HERE'S THE 5-DAY FORECAST!" I MEAN, WHERE'S THE **ENERGY?**

ALL I'M ASKING FOR IS A LITTLE **PASSION,** WINK! A LITTLE **EMOTION!**

@ # !
? ● *

WHEN IT RAINS, IT POURS!

AL ROKER WOULD NEVER USE THAT KIND OF LANGUAGE.

SCHOOL PICTURE GUY! WHAT ARE **YOU** DOING AT THE BEACH?

IT'S CALLED MAKING A LIVING, KID!

I'M ATTEMPTING TO LURE POTENTIAL PATRONS TO A FINE DINING ESTABLISH— MENT CALLED **CAP'N SALTY'S!**

BY WEAR- ING A **COS- TUME?**

EXACTLY, LAD! PEOPLE SEE ME AND IMMEDIATELY THINK OF MOUTHWATERING **SEAFOOD!**

TODAY'S SPECIAL: FRIED CLAMS

MOMMY, LOOK AT THE FAT SPIDER!

MADAM, KINDLY INFORM THE CHILD THAT I AM A LOBSTER.

SCHOOL PICTURE GUY, HOW COME YOU'RE WORKING FOR CAP'N SALTY'S? ISN'T THAT SORT OF A DIVE?

A DIVE?

IT'S **AUTHENTIC**, IF THAT'S WHAT YOU MEAN! IT'S A REAL, OLD-FASHIONED SEAFOOD SHACK!

IT'S NOT LIKE THOSE INFERNAL **CHAIN** RESTAURANTS WITH THEIR TV JINGLES, MOLDED PLASTIC SEATS AND INSIPID CARTOON **MASCOTS**!

BUT... AREN'T **YOU** A MASCOT?

I'M A GOODWILL AMBASSADOR, KID. I'VE GOT DIGNITY.

Peire

WELL, HI THERE, NATE! HOW ARE YOU?

I JUST SAW SOMETHING THAT KIND OF BUMMED ME OUT, MR. ROSA.

HOT LI

YOU KNOW THE SCHOOL PICTURE GUY? HE'S DRESSED UP IN A **LOBSTER SUIT** TO ADVERTISE **CAP'N SALTY'S!**

TO SEE SOMEBODY WORKING SOME CHEESY JOB BECAUSE THEY DON'T EARN ENOUGH AT THEIR **REAL** JOB... IT WAS SORT OF DE-PRESSING, YOU KNOW?

ANYWAY!... CAN I HAVE TWO SCOOPS OF ROCKY ROAD IN A SUGAR CONE?

UH-HUH.

HOT LI

HI, MR. EUSTIS! WOULD YOU LIKE TO BUY SOME WRAPPING PAPER TO SUPPORT...?

WHOA, THERE! HOLD IT, NATE!

LAST YEAR YOU TOLD ME THAT IF I BOUGHT SOME OF YOUR SCENTED CANDLES, YOU'D NEVER TRY TO SELL ME ANYTHING AGAIN!

RIGHT. BUT THAT WAS FOR THE CHESS TEAM. THIS IS FOR MY SCOUT TROOP.

GOT ME WITH THE OL' BAIT AND SWITCH.

"PASTEL POTPOURRI" OR "SCRATCH 'N' SNIFF"?

Peirce

HI, MISTER, I'M SELLING WRAPPING PAPER FOR THE JUNIOR WOODCHUCKS, AND...

WOOD-CHUCKS, YOU SAY?

THIS DOESN'T LOOK LIKE A WOODCHUCK! THIS LOOKS MORE LIKE AN EAST INDIAN **BANDICOOT!**

SLAM!

EITHER WE REDESIGN OUR LOGO OR WE STOP TRYING TO SELL STUFF TO ZOOLOGISTS.

I THOUGHT YOU GUYS WERE GONNA PLAY SOME BASKETBALL!

WE ARE.

THEN LET'S GO! I'LL BE KEVIN GARNETT!

I'LL BE CARMELO ANTHONY.

AND I'M CARMELO'S AGENT.

HM? AGENT?

I'D LIKE TO ANNOUNCE THAT CARMELO IS HOLDING OUT.

HE'S LOOKING FOR A NEW LONG-TERM DEAL, SO I'VE ADVISED HIM THAT PLAYING BASKETBALL AT THIS TIME IS NOT IN HIS BEST INTEREST.

DO **YOU** WANT TO PLAY BASKETBALL?

WE'RE CARMELO'S ENTOURAGE.

WHAT ARE YOU SITTING AROUND FOR? I THOUGHT WE AGREED YOU WERE GOING TO DO SOMETHING TO EARN MONEY!

I AM!

IF I'M THE NINETY-NINTH CALLER TO THE RADIO STATION, I'LL WIN NINETY-NINE DOLLARS!

beep boop beep boop

DANG! IT'S BUSY!

...UNLIKE YOU.

NO WORRIES, DAD. THEY RUN THE CONTEST EVERY HOUR.

HOW'S THE MONEY-MAKING GOING?

IT'S NOT GOING AT ALL.

WHAT ABOUT MY SUGGESTION THAT YOU SET UP A LEMONADE STAND?

UH, SLIGHT PROBLEM THERE, DAD.

WE HAVE NO LEMONADE MIX IN THE HOUSE. WE HAVE NO LEMONS. WE HAVE NO SUGAR.

I HAVEN'T BEEN SHOPPING IN A WHILE.

...BUT WE'VE GOT **SOY SAUCE!** MMMMMM! RE**FRESH**ING!

ELLEN, CAN YOU **PLEASE** LEND ME TEN BUCKS? PLEEEEEZ!? COME **ON**, WE'RE **BLOOD**! WE'RE **FAMILY**!

ALL **RIGHT**! ALL RIGHT, ALREADY!

JUST DON'T FORGET THAT LAST WORD.

WHAT... FAMILY?

BLOOD.

!

SEEING "THE OTHER GUYS" SEEMS A LOT LESS IMPORTANT THAN IT DID A MINUTE AGO.

Panel 1: HOW MUCH FOR A SMALL POPCORN? / WE DON'T HAVE SMALL. WE HAVE LARGE, SUPER AND JUMBO.

Panel 2: SO... A LARGE IS LIKE A SMALL? / NO.

Panel 3: LARGE IS THE NEW MEDIUM, SUPER IS THE NEW LARGE, AND JUMBO IS THE NEW EXTRA LARGE.

Panel 4: THIS IS THE NEW LAME. / HOW MUCH FOR A BOX OF "GOOBERS"? / MINI, MAXI OR MEGA?

I CAN'T BELIEVE YOU'RE **INSIDE** ON SUCH A BEAUTIFUL DAY!

YOU SHOULD BE OUTSIDE **PLAYING** SPORTS, NOT **WATCHING** THEM ON TV!

I'M NOT WATCHING SPORTS. I'M WATCHING "JERSEY SHORE."

NOT FOR LONG.

IT ONLY **LOOKS** LIKE SPORTS BECAUSE THEY TAKE THEIR BEACH VOLLEYBALL SO SERIOUSLY.

Peirce

MRS. WINSLOW USED TO HIRE **ME** TO MOW HER LAWN, BUT NOW SHE USES A **LANDSCAPING SERVICE!**

THOSE GUYS ARE **EXPENSIVE!** THEY CHARGE **WAY** MORE THAN **I** DO!

I WONDER WHY SHE MADE THE SWITCH.

PERHAPS IT'S A "QUALITY-OF-WORK" ISSUE.

OKAY, SO I RAN OVER ONE OF HER STUPID LAWN GNOMES.

THAT WAS AN **ACCIDENT!**

IF YOU HAD TO CHOOSE ONE PLACE TO GO, WHERE WOULD IT BE?

ITALY!

THE GONDOLAS OF VENICE! THE LEANING TOWER OF PISA! THE RUINS OF POMPEII! ITALY WOULD BE **GREAT!**

BUT SPAIN WOULD BE COOL, TOO! THE ARCHITECTURE IN BARCELONA IS SUPPOSED TO BE **SPECTACULAR!**

...OR WHAT ABOUT **CHINA?** I'VE ALWAYS WANTED TO WALK ON THE GREAT WALL!

AND THEN THERE'S AUSTRALIA! SYDNEY IS ONE OF THE...

FRANCIS! **FRANCIS!**

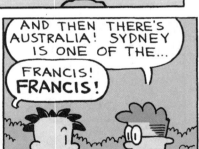

I MEANT, CHOOSE ONE PLACE AROUND **HERE!**... **TODAY!**

I'M THINKING ARCADE!

OH, AND CAN I HAVE SOME MONEY?

WHAT ARE YOU WORK-ING ON?

MY NEW COMIC BOOK, TEDDY!

I'M CREATING MY OWN SUPERHEROINE, JUST LIKE "FEMME FATALITY"!

UH... NOT **JUST** LIKE FEMME FATALITY.

HM?

THAT'S ONE BIG BUTT, DUDE.

ex**CUSE** ME, THAT'S HER **TURBO FANNY PACK**!

I NEED TO COME UP WITH A NAME FOR THE STAR OF MY COMIC BOOK.

A GREAT NAME IS ONE OF THE REASONS "FEMME FATALITY" IS SO POPULAR! BUT I JUST CAN'T **THINK** OF ANYTHING!

ARRGH! AND NOW I JUST TOTALLY MESSED UP HER FACE!

HOW ABOUT "FEMME FUTILITY"?

...OR "LADY GARGOYLE"!

ERASE ERASE ERASE ERASE

Peirce

NATE! STILL WORKING ON "EVE OF DESTRUCTION"?

SORT OF.

I DECIDED TO CHANGE EVE TO A **MALE** CHARACTER!

SO YOU STARTED OVER?

NO, NO... I JUST MADE A FEW TWEAKS TO WHAT I ALREADY DID!

"STEVE OF DESTRUCTION".

TWO EXTRA LETTERS, SOME 5 O'CLOCK SHADOW, AND WE'RE GOOD TO GO!

Peirce

HI, NATE!

GORDIE, MY MAN! I HAVE A BUSINESS PROPOSITION!

LET'S HEAR IT!

I'VE WRITTEN MY OWN COMIC BOOK, "STEVE OF DESTRUCTION"! HOW ABOUT YOU SELL IT HERE AT "KLASSIC KOMIX"?

HM... AND HOW MUCH DO YOU THINK I SHOULD CHARGE?

A **LOT**! BECAUSE THAT'S THE **ORIGINAL** ARTWORK!

YES, I NOTICED THE CHEESE DOODLE STAINS.

ExACTLY! THOSE MAKE IT A **COLLECTOR'S** ITEM!

AH! I SEE YOU'RE A FAN OF ADVENTURE COMIC BOOKS, MISTER!

UH... YEAH.

WELL, THEN, YOU MIGHT ENJOY **THIS** BRAND-NEW CREATION! IT'S CALLED "STEVE OF DESTRUCTION"!

THIS LOOKS LIKE SOMETHING A TEN-YEAR-OLD KID DREW IN HIS NOTEBOOK WITH A BALL-POINT PEN.

YOUR FIRST REVIEW!

FOR THE **RECORD**, PAL, I'M **ELEVEN!**

THE WATER'S SO **WARM** TODAY!

HEY!

NARF NARF NARF NARF

GET OUT OF HERE! **BEAT IT!!**

SKWAK!

LOOK AT THAT! IT ATE ALL MY PEANUT BUTTER CUPS! IT TORE OPEN MY BAG OF CHEEZ DOODLES!

STUPID BIRD! STUPID, STUPID BIRD!

SKWEE

WHY DIDN'T IT EAT **YOUR** LUNCH?

BEATS ME! THERE'S LOTS OF YUMMY STUFF HERE!

AN EGG SALAD SANDWICH, BROWN RICE WITH GOAT CHEESE, ARTICHOKE HEARTS AND SOME SOY MILK!

SORRY.

FRANCIS, WE'VE BEEN HERE FOR **TWO HOURS!**

I KNOW, BUT IT'S SO HARD TO **DECIDE!**

SHOULD I GO WITH A **SOFT** PENCIL CASE OR A **HARD** PENCIL CASE?

LEMME SEE.

THWAK!

HARD.

I'M REALLY HAPPY WITH THE BINDER I BOUGHT!

YOU ALREADY TOLD ME THAT, FRANCIS.

DID I **ALSO** TELL YOU HOW MUCH I LOVE THE SOUND OF THE VELCRO POCKETS OPENING AND CLOSING?

RRIP!...SHUCK!
RRIP!...SHUCK!
RRIP!...SHUCK!
RRIP!...SHUCK!

RRIP!... SHUCK! RRIP!...
SHUCK!
RRIP!...
SHUCK
RRIP!...
SHUCK!... RRI
RRIP
SHU
RRI
SHU
RR
SHU
RRI

I HATE THIS TIME OF YEAR.

Peirce

WHAT THE...?

NATE, WHAT ARE YOU **DOING**? IT'S **5:00 A.M.**!

EXACTLY. I'M STARTING EARLY.

STARTING **WHAT** EARLY?

ANYTHING! **EVERY**THING!

THIS IS MY LAST DAY OF FREEDOM BEFORE SCHOOL STARTS, DAD! I INTEND TO LIVE IT TO THE **FULLEST**!

I'M GOING TO THE BEACH, THE ARCADE, THE MINI GOLF COURSE, THE ICE CREAM SHOP...

NATE, NONE OF THOSE PLACES ARE OPEN UNTIL 9 OR 10.

OH.

WELL, SINCE YOU'RE UP, CAN YOU MAKE ME SOME BACON AND EGGS?

APPARENTLY, THAT WHOLE "BREAKFAST IS THE MOST IM- PORTANT MEAL OF THE DAY" THING IS COMPLETELY BOGUS.

I AM **SO** EXCITED ABOUT THE START OF THIS SCHOOL YEAR!

WE'VE EXPANDED THE LIBRARY, WE'VE INSTALLED NEW LOCK-ERS, WE'VE UPGRADED OUR COMPUTER LAB!

THE BUILDING HAS NEVER LOOKED BETTER! WAIT 'TIL THE KIDS SEE ALL THIS!

THIS STINKIN' DUMP NEVER CHANGES.

ARRRGH! I'M IN MRS. GODFREY'S HOMEROOM!

THERE ARE **SEVEN** HOMEROOMS IN THE SIXTH GRADE, AND OF COURSE I END UP IN **HERS**!

I'M NOT EXACTLY DOING CARTWHEELS ABOUT IT MYSELF.

NOT ONLY AM I IN HER HOMEROOM, NOW I'VE GOT A PICTURE OF HER DOING CARTWHEELS STUCK IN MY HEAD.

MY MOM'S GONNA **KILL** ME!

WHAT'S UP, LADIES?

SHEILA LOST AN EARRING.

AND I JUST **GOT** THEM **YES**TERDAY!

AH! NO WORRIES, SHEILA!

I'LL SAVE THE DAY WITH MY AMAZING SENSE OF **SMELL**!

JUST LET ME TAKE A WHIFF OF **THIS** ONE...

SNIFF!

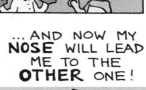

...AND NOW MY **NOSE** WILL LEAD ME TO THE **OTHER** ONE!

SNIFF Snuff

SNIFF SNIFFA SNIFFA SNIFF

SNIFF SNIFF SNIFF SNIFF

!

I FOUND IT, BUT TRUST ME: YOU DON'T WANT TO WEAR IT EVER AGAIN.

MR. ROSA, ARE WE GONNA TAKE ANY FIELD TRIPS THIS YEAR?

WE'LL HAVE TO WAIT AND SEE, NATE.

HUH? WAIT AND SEE ABOUT **WHAT**?

GIVE ME ONE GOOD REASON WHY WE SHOULDN'T VISIT THE ART MUSEUM!

KLUNK!

I'M SURE I'LL THINK OF ONE.

WHAT IDIOT PUT **THAT** THERE?

Peirce

WHAT'S GOING ON?

YOU TOLD ME TO CLEAN UP THE ATTIC, SO I'M HAVING A YARD SALE!

WHOA, **WHOA!** YOU ARE **NOT** SELLING **THIS!**

WHAT'S **THAT** THING?

THE "BUCK UP" AWARD! FROM MY HIGH SCHOOL HOCKEY DAYS!

OUR TEAM WAS CALLED THE BUCKS! THAT'S WHY OUR COACH CREATED THIS **ANTLER** TROPHY!

IT WAS GIVEN TO THE PLAYER WHO SHOWED THE MOST GRIT AND DETERMIN-ATION!

I'LL **KEEP** THIS, THANK YOU VERY MUCH! THIS IS THE ONLY AWARD I'VE EVER WON!

IT'S **PRICELESS!**

T**R**IP!

WILL YOU TAKE A DOLLAR FOR THIS?

SOLD.

YOU KNOW WHAT LOSES SOCCER GAMES, BOYS? **POOR CONDITIONING!**

AND HOW DO YOU **COMBAT** POOR CONDITIONING? BY GETTING IN **TIP-TOP SHAPE!**

AND HOW DO YOU **GET** IN TIP-TOP SHAPE? BY **RUNNING!**

IF HE ALREADY KNOWS THE ANSWERS, WHY IS HE ASKING THE QUESTIONS?

WHAT **KIND** OF RUN-NING?...

WHIMPER

YOU KNOW WHAT YOUR PROBLEM IS, NANCY BOYS? YOU ALL THINK **SPORTS** ARE SUPPOSED TO BE **FUN!**

NO! THAT'S **WRONG!** SPORTS ARE FUN IF YOU **WIN!** WINNING IS FUN! **LOSING** IS **NOT** FUN!

WHAT ABOUT TIES?

"WHAT ABOUT TIES" **RUN,** WISE GUY!!

COACH? HOW MUCH LONGER IS PRACTICE GONNA LAST?

AS LONG AS IT TAKES, SOLDIER.

SEE, YOU CAN PRACTICE HARD AND BECOME GOOD PLAYERS... YOU CAN PRACTICE **HARDER** AND BECOME **GREAT** PLAYERS...

... OR YOU CAN **PUSH** YOURSELVES TO THE **MAX** AND BECOME **LEGENDS!**

ACTUALLY, I'M OKAY WITH NOT BEING A LEGEND.

YEAH, I'M NOT REALLY THE LEGEND TYPE.

I'M HUNGRY.

CRIPES.

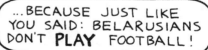

WHOA, WHOA! MRS. GODFREY HAS WON TWO "TEACHER OF THE YEAR" AWARDS??

SHE HAS INDEED!

ACCORDING TO **WHO?**

THE SCHOOL BOARD!

OH. WELL, THAT EXPLAINS IT.

THAT'S THE SAME GROUP OF IDIOTS WHO OUTLAWED "DODGEBALL".

Peirce

I'M POSTING AN ANGRY BLOG ENTRY ABOUT MRS. GODFREY WINNING TWO "TEACHER OF THE YEAR" AWARDS.

SHE'S NOT THE BEST TEACHER IN THE SCHOOL. NOT EVEN **CLOSE!**

SCHOOL? THAT AWARD COVERS THE ENTIRE **DISTRICT!**

TIME TO BREAK OUT THE EMOTICONS.

HE'S EASILY OUT-RAGED.

WHAT DO YOU THINK?

ABOUT WHAT?

ABOUT THIS **SHOT!** IS IT A SIX IRON OR A SEVEN IRON?

IT DOESN'T REALLY MATTER.

DOESN'T **MATTER?**

RIGHT.

NATE, A CADDY IS SUPPOSED TO BRING SOME **INSIGHT** TO THE TABLE!

THAT **IS** MY INSIGHT!

I'M TELLING YOU THAT, WHETHER YOU HIT A SIX OR A SEVEN, THE RESULT WILL BE THE SAME.

GEE, THANKS **SO** MUCH.

I'LL HIT THE SEVEN.

HA CK!

ACTUALLY, I WAS THINKING YOU'D PUT IT IN THE WATER, BUT THIS PROVES MY POINT TOO.

WHAT ARE YOU DOING?

JUST CHECKING OUT MY HOROSCOPE!

YOU'RE NOT SUPPOSED TO USE SCHOOL COMPUTERS FOR STUFF LIKE THAT.

OH, RELAX, FRANCIS! THIS'LL ONLY TAKE A SECOND!

"TROUBLE WILL ARRIVE UNEXPECTEDLY."

THAT'S THE LAMEST HOROSCOPE I'VE EVER READ.

I'M HERE FOR DETENTION, MRS. CZERWICKI.

OH, DEAR. WHAT IS IT **THIS** TIME, NATE?

MRS. GODFREY CAUGHT ME USING A SCHOOL COMPUTER TO READ MY HOROSCOPE... BUT WHAT'S SO BAD ABOUT **THAT**?

I MEAN, **EVERY**BODY LIKES TO READ HOROSCOPES! EVERYBODY WANTS TO... TOOooo...

NATE WRIGHT. SCORPIO.

SIT DOWN, CHILD.

Peirce

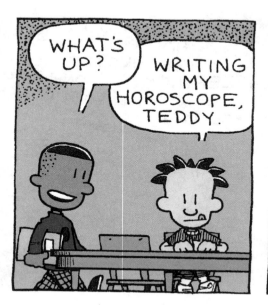

WHAT'S UP?

WRITING MY HOROSCOPE, TEDDY.

YOU MEAN **READING** YOUR HORO-SCOPE.

NO, I'M DONE WITH THAT. I GOT SICK OF ALL THOSE DOOM AND GLOOM PRE-DICTIONS.

IT'S WAY MORE FUN TO JUST WRITE 'EM MY **SELF!**

"SUPERSTARDOM IS IMMINENT."

PLUS, MINE ARE SO **ACCURATE!**

Peirce

Panel 1:

I'VE STARTED A BUSINESS SELLING HOROSCOPES! I WRITE 'EM MY- SELF!

FOR A **DOLLAR**?

HOROSCOPES
ONLY $1.00

Panel 2:

WHY WOULD ANYBODY **PAY** YOU FOR A HOROSCOPE?

BECAUSE UNLIKE **NEWSPAPER** HOROSCOPES, **MINE** ARE **PERSONALIZED**! HERE!

Panel 3:

"TODAY FOR LUNCH, YOU WILL HAVE A TUNA SANDWICH, BLUEBERRY YOGURT, CELERY AND A PEANUT BUTTER COOKIE."

Panel 4:

THAT'S WHAT I'VE HAD FOR LUNCH EVERY DAY SINCE SECOND GRADE.

EXACTLY! DOES A **NEWSPAPER** HAVE THAT KIND OF KNOWLEDGE?

ONE DOLLAR, PLEASE.

ISBN 978-0-545-84290-7

12 11 10 9 8 7 6 5 4 3 2 1   15 16 17 18 19 20/0

Printed in the U.S.A.   40

First Scholastic printing, January 2015

These strips appeared in newspapers from March 8, 2010, through October 9, 2010.